Hans-Günter Heumann

Piano Junior

A Creative and Interactive
Piano Course for Children

Lesson Book 2

ED 13802

Illustrations by Leopé

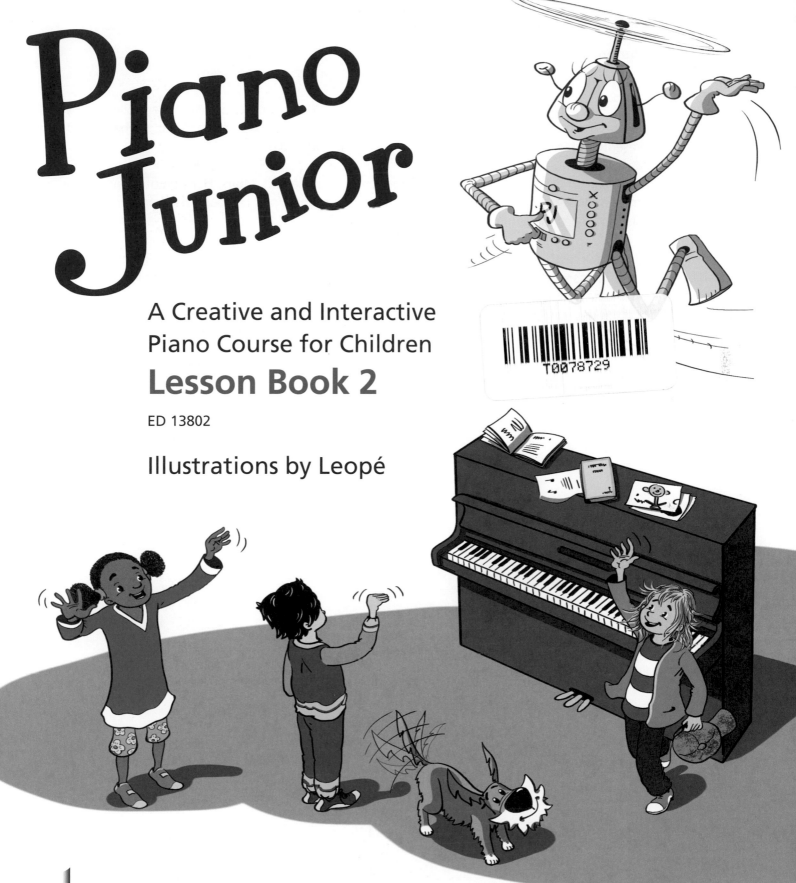

SCHOTT

Mainz · London · Berlin · Madrid · New York · Paris · Prague · Tokyo · Toronto

About the Author

Hans-Günter Heumann is a freelance composer and author, living in southern Germany.

Since studying piano, composition, and music pedagogy at the Musikhochschule Hannover, followed by further studies in the USA, he has dedicated himself to the editing of pedagogical piano material. He has a particular interest in presenting music in an accessible way to reach a broad audience.

Based on many years of experience teaching children, young people and adults, Hans-Günter has written a great number of internationally successful and award winning publications, and has composed and arranged piano music in a range of styles for beginners to advanced students.

Having developed successful, methodical concepts for learning how to play the piano for all age groups and abilities, Hans-Günter's work has been translated into many different languages and sold millions of copies, an indication of the wide-spread appreciation of his work.
His publications *Klavierspielen – mein schönstes Hobby* and *Piano Kids* (both published by Schott Music) have become two of the most significant piano methods in the German language.

Acknowledgments

The author and publishers would like to thank Prof. Carolyn True, Melanie Spanswick and Dr. Sally Cathcart for expert suggestions, support and advice in the development of *Piano Junior*.

ED 13802
British Library Cataloguing-in-Publication Data.
A catalogue record for this book is available from the British Library
ISMN 979-0-2201-3637-5
ISBN 978-1-84761-426-1

English translation: Schott London Editorial
Design by Barbara Brümmer
Typesetting Elke Göpfert
Music setting: Darius-Heise-Krzyszton
Stockphotos: Icons (Playing Corner, Composing Corner,)
Cover design: www.adamhaystudio.com
Audio tracks recorded, mixed and mastered by Clements Pianos
Audio tracks performed by Samantha Ward and Maciej Raginia
Printed in Germany S&Co. 9201

Introduction

Piano Junior is a creative and interactive piano course for children from the age of 6, which progresses in small, manageable steps. It is a fun and satisfying approach to playing and learning about music, encouraging quick and noticeable progress.

Piano Junior is home to PJ, a robot with great enthusiasm for the piano, who accompanies and motivates children throughout the piano course. On PJ's homepage **www.piano-junior.com** you will find audio tracks of all pieces played on an acoustic piano, further fun practise resources and other interactive elements.

This innovative course stimulates and encourages creativity through regular, integrated 'Corners', such as, *Composing, Improvising, Action, Playing, Technique, Ear Training, Memory, Sight-Reading* and *Music Quizzes*. In this way solid musical knowledge and technical ability is acquired. The experience of learning the piano is multifaceted: aural – with regular ear-training exercises; visual – with sight-reading; tactile – with clear explanations of technical aspects of playing and, above all, creative – with exercises in composing and improvising.

The choice of pieces includes attractive pieces from the classical period to the present day as well as interesting arrangements of folk tunes and children's songs, classical masterpieces, jazz and pop melodies.

In addition to the **Lesson Book** (which includes Exercises) at each level there is also: a **Theory Book**, in which valuable information from the method is worked through and consolidated in a playful, imaginative way. There is also a **Duet Book** at each level, to provide motivation for playing the piano with others and a **Performance Book** with great repertoire, which is fun to play. The *Flash Cards* included can be used to provide further practice in note reading, with musical symbols/terms and with rhythm patterns. By collecting the cards from each volume you will acquire a wealth of reference material.

Music greatly enriches the life of a child and **Piano Junior** aims to provide a musical basis for this in the most creative and motivating way.

Hans-Günter Heumann

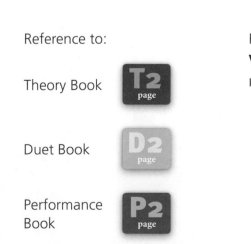

Reference to:

Theory Book **T2** page

Duet Book **D2** page

Performance Book **P2** page

References to material at
www.piano-junior.com:

▶ Audio Track **1** | Rhythm Check **1** | Workout **1** | Sight-Reading **1**

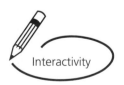

Interactivity

Contents

Summary of Book 1

Fingering

Black Keys

Notes and one Rest

count: 1 2 3 4

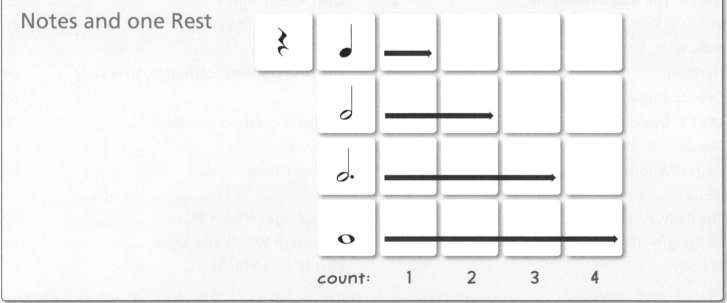

Lines and Spaces

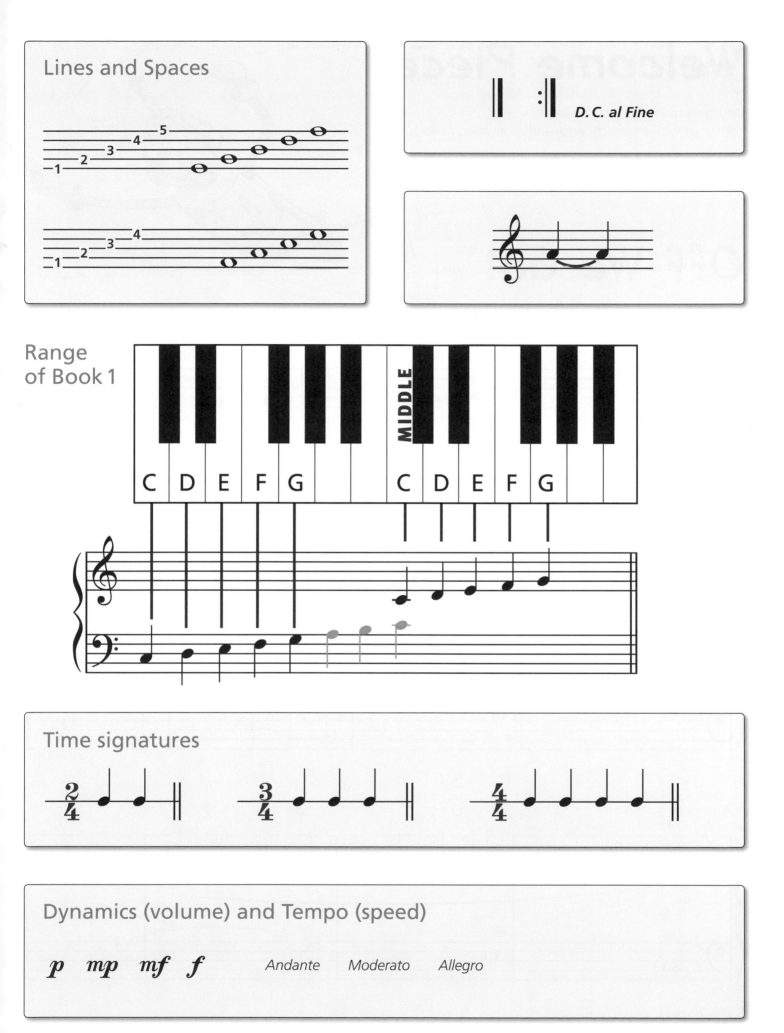

D. C. al Fine

Range of Book 1

Time signatures

Dynamics (volume) and Tempo (speed)

𝒑 𝒎𝒑 𝒎𝒇 𝒇   *Andante*   *Moderato*   *Allegro*

Welcome Piece

Welcome to PIANO JUNIOR level 2!
Let's start with a very cheerful and motivating melody.

Off We Go!

Allegro

HGH

Name notes

Prepare to jump

▶ Audio Track **1** | Rhythm Check **1** | Workout **1**

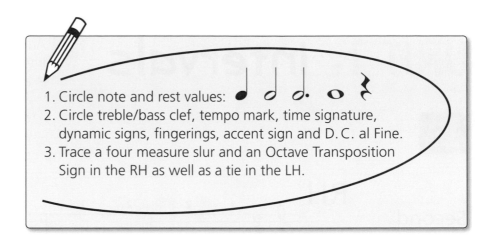

1. Circle note and rest values:
2. Circle treble/bass clef, tempo mark, time signature, dynamic signs, fingerings, accent sign and D. C. al Fine.
3. Trace a four measure slur and an Octave Transposition Sign in the RH as well as a tie in the LH.

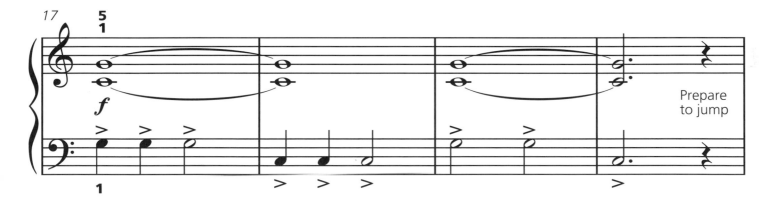

Prepare to jump

Fine

Prepare to jump

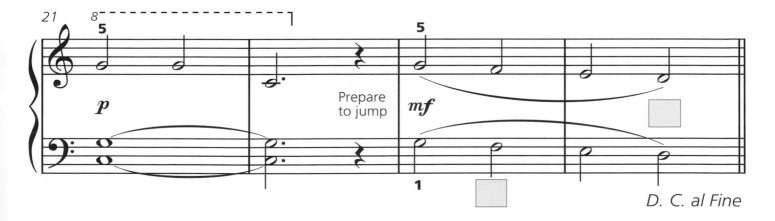

Prepare to jump

D. C. al Fine

9

UNIT 1: Intervals

T2 page 6/7

An **interval** is the distance between two notes. Intervals are heard as:
- a **melodic interval**. Two notes sound one after another as a melody, either upwards or downwards.
- an **harmonic interval**. Two notes sound together, producing harmony.

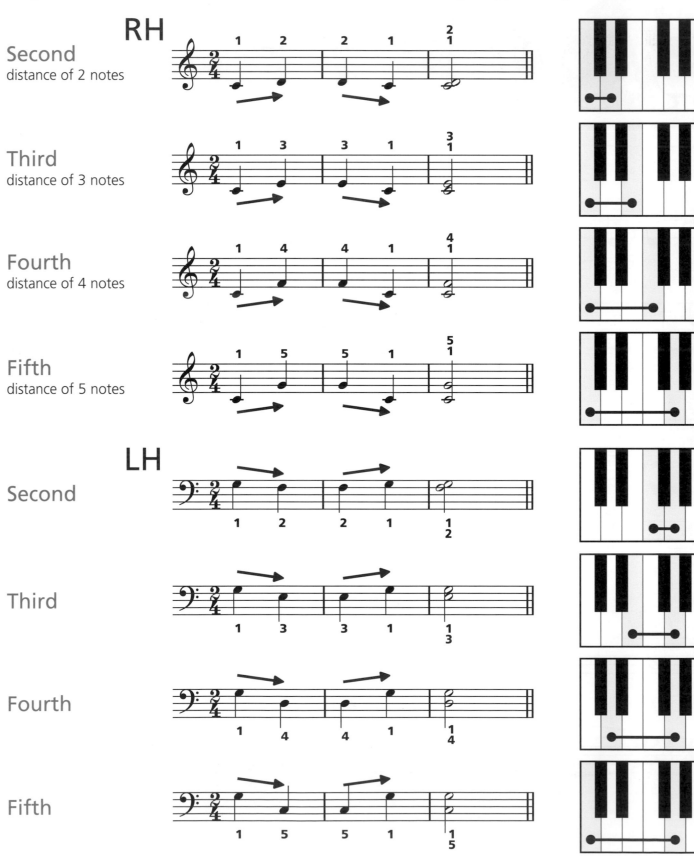

RH

Second distance of 2 notes

Third distance of 3 notes

Fourth distance of 4 notes

Fifth distance of 5 notes

LH

Second

Third

Fourth

Fifth

Interval Excercise

Finger Fitness page 70/71, No. 1–3

HGH

C 5-Finger Position

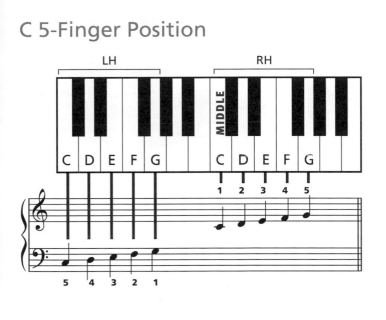

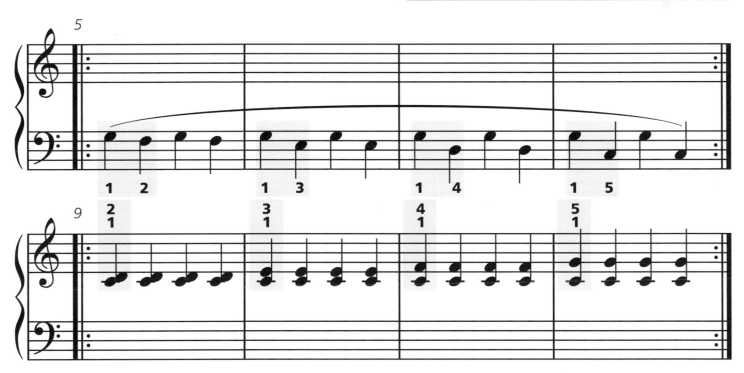

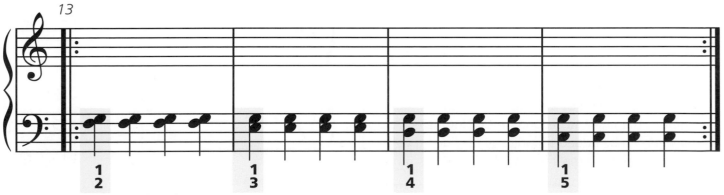

▶ Audio Track **2** | Workout **2** | Sight Reading **1–6**

Coming and Going

 D2 page 4/5 **P2** page 4 **Finger Fitness** page 71/72, No. 4–6

Moderato

HGH

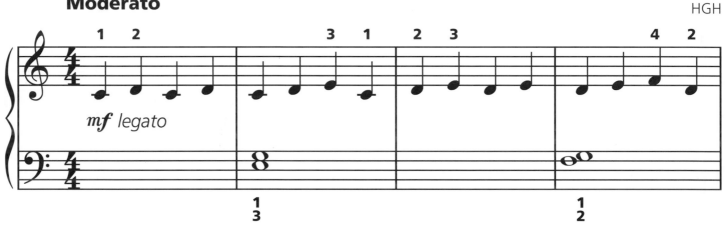

mf legato

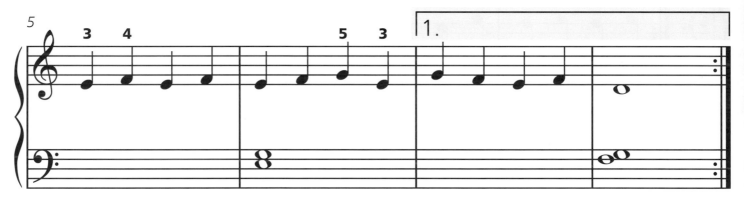

Bracket 1|2

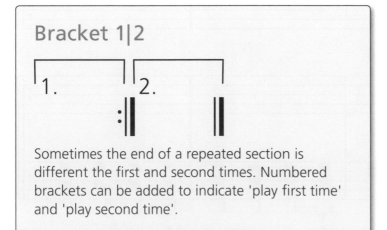

Sometimes the end of a repeated section is different the first and second times. Numbered brackets can be added to indicate 'play first time' and 'play second time'.

7b

▶ Audio Track **3** | Workout **3**

The Juggler

P2 page 5 · Finger Fitness · page 73, No. 7

> **Ternary Form: A–B–A**
>
> **Ternary form** is a type of structure in three parts.
> It has an **A–B–A** shape:
> Theme **A** is introduced, followed by a contrasting
> **B** theme, before returning to the **A** theme again.

HGH

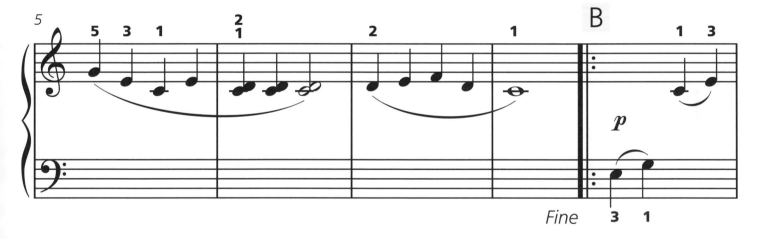

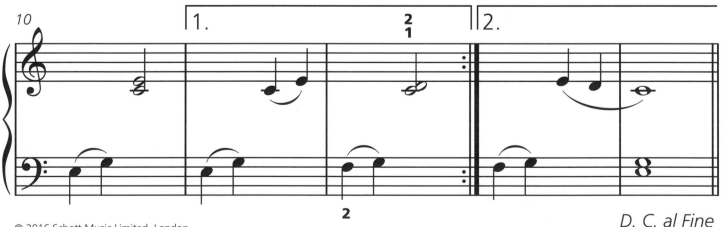

D. C. al Fine

The Merry-Go-Round

T2 page 8/9 P2 page 6

Allegro

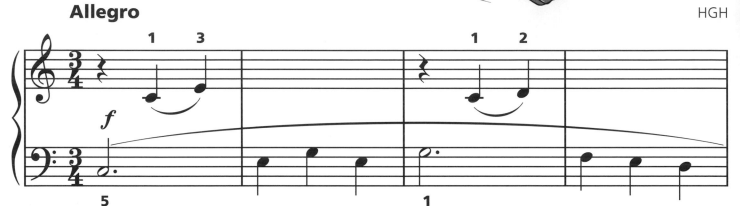

Fine

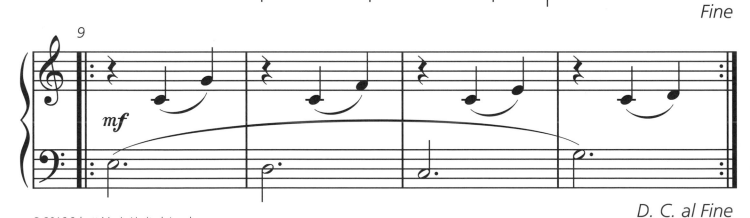

D. C. al Fine

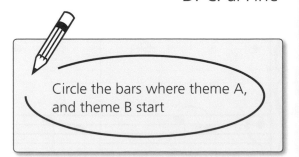

Circle the bars where theme A, and theme B start

▶ Audio Track **5** | Rhythm Check **2**

The Class Clown

Upbeat

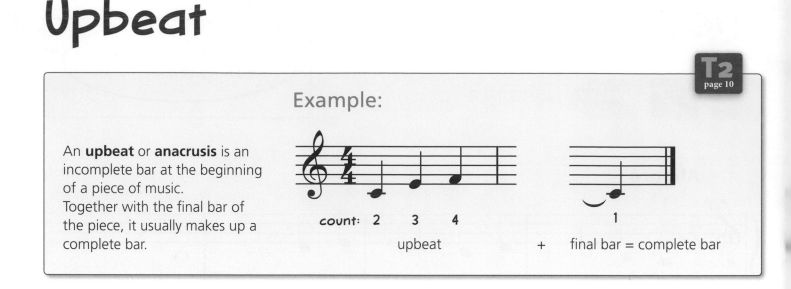

Example:

An **upbeat** or **anacrusis** is an incomplete bar at the beginning of a piece of music.
Together with the final bar of the piece, it usually makes up a complete bar.

count: 2 3 4

upbeat + final bar = complete bar

When the Saints Go Marching In

Allegro

Traditional / American Gospel Hymn
Arr.: HGH

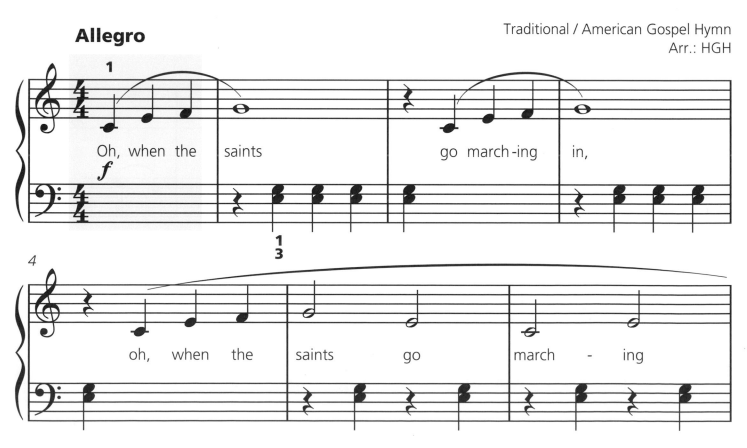

Oh, when the saints go march-ing in,

oh, when the saints go march - ing

▶ Audio Track **7** | Rhythm Check **3** | Workout **5**

in,⎯⎯⎯ I want to be

in that num - ber,⎯⎯⎯ when the

saints go march - ing in.⎯⎯⎯

Beautiful Day

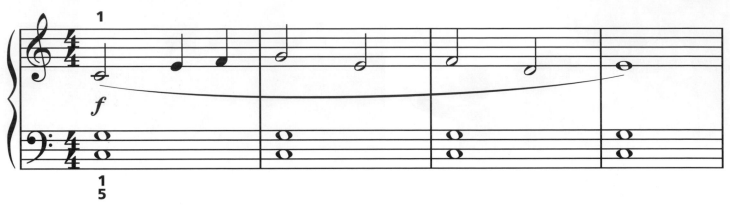

Andante

HGH

Fine

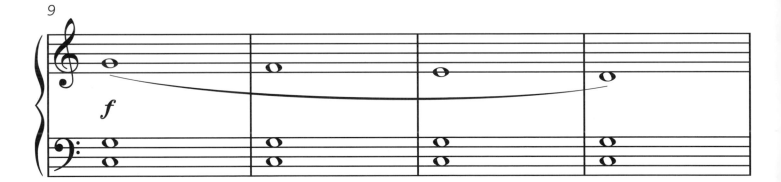

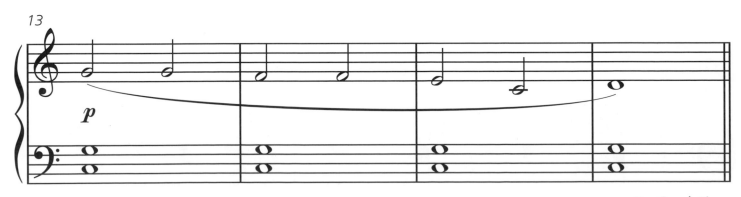

D. C. al Fine

18

▶ Audio Track **8**

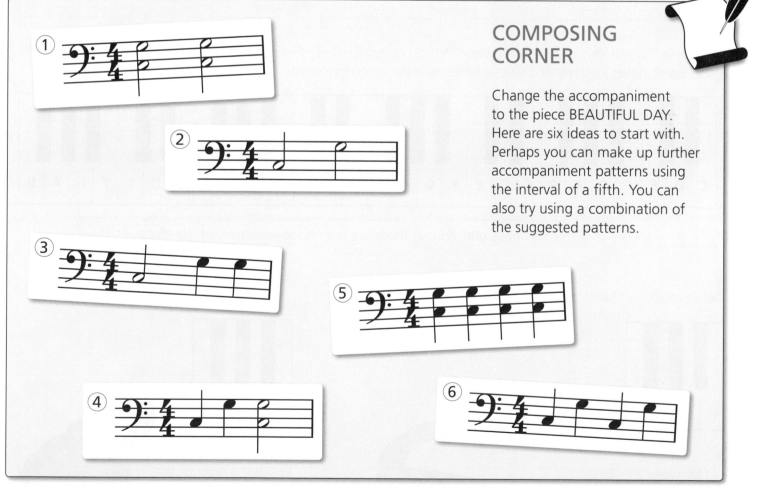

COMPOSING CORNER

Change the accompaniment to the piece BEAUTIFUL DAY. Here are six ideas to start with. Perhaps you can make up further accompaniment patterns using the interval of a fifth. You can also try using a combination of the suggested patterns.

UNIT 2: Seven White Keys
C–D–E–F–G–A–B

T2 page 12

Three White Keys + **Four White Keys**

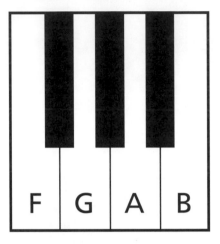

Three white keys form a group around the two black keys:
C-D-E

Four white keys form a group around the three black keys:
F-G-A-B

These seven white keys are the seven basic musical notes: C–D–E–F–G–A–B
These seven notes are repeated several times over the piano keyboard.

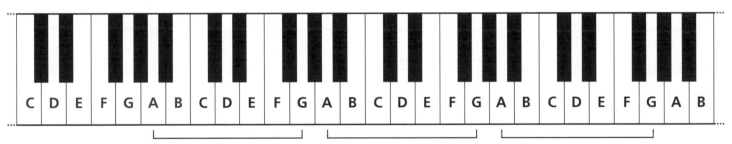

You may have noticed that these are the first seven letters of the alphabet.

Pay attention to the two new notes: **A–B**

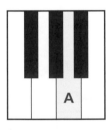

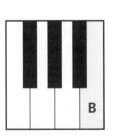

A
lies between the 2nd and 3rd keys of the group of three black notes

B
lies to the right of the group of three black notes

20

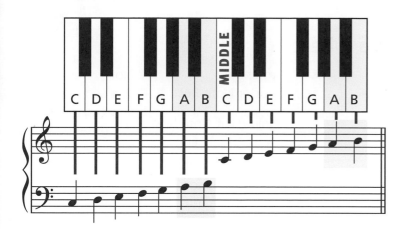

Play Seven Notes

P2 page 8/9

HGH

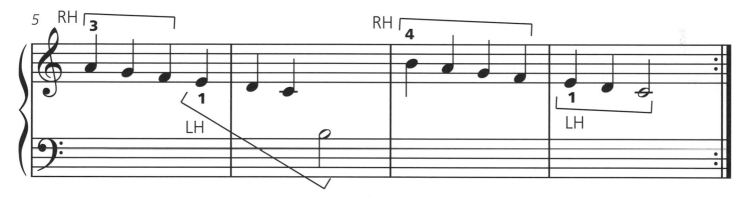

© 2016 Schott Music Limited, London

Accompaniment

© 2016 Schott Music Limited, London

UNIT 3: Rests

Rests are used in music to indicate moments of silence in the melody or accompaniment. The fingers are lifted from the keys.
Each note has an equivalent rest.

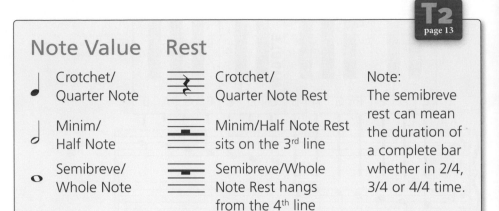

T2 page 13

Note Value		Rest	
♩	Crotchet/ Quarter Note	𝄾	Crotchet/ Quarter Note Rest
♩	Minim/ Half Note	▬	Minim/Half Note Rest sits on the 3rd line
𝅝	Semibreve/ Whole Note	▬	Semibreve/Whole Note Rest hangs from the 4th line

Note:
The semibreve rest can mean the duration of a complete bar whether in 2/4, 3/4 or 4/4 time.

Are you Tired? Have a Break!

P2 page 10/11

Andante

HGH

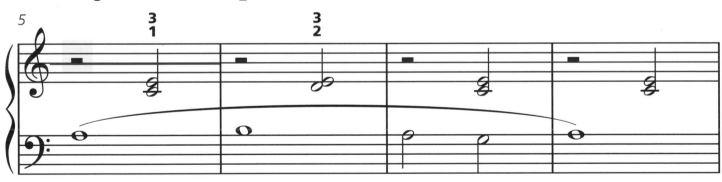

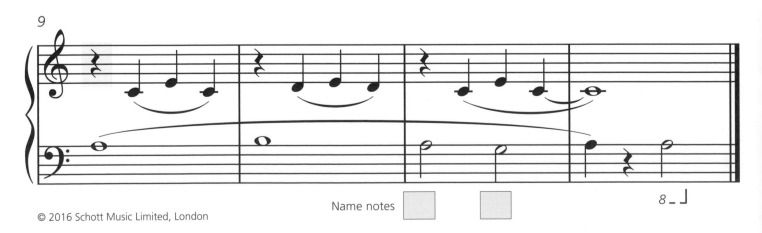

Name notes

22

▶ Audio Track **11** | Rhythm Check **4** | Sight Reading **7**

The Singing Goose Girl

T2 page 14/15 **P2** p. 12 above

Finger Fitness page 74, No. 9

Moderato

HGH

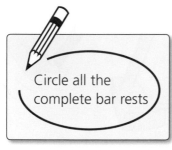

Circle all the complete bar rests

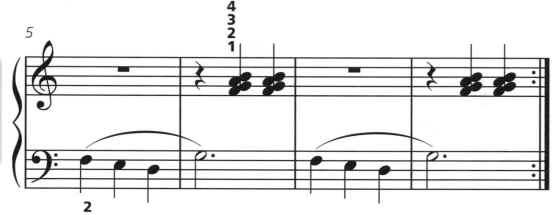

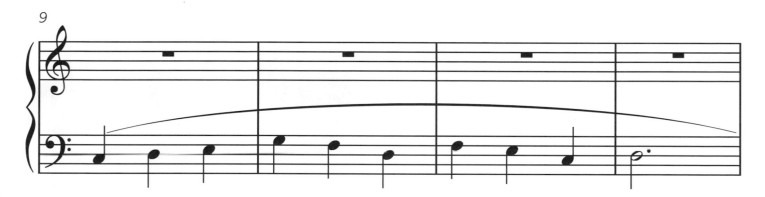

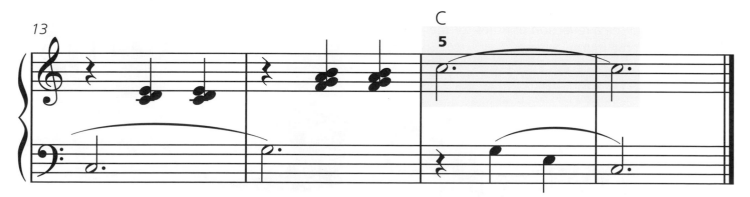

*) A **cluster**, or **note cluster**, is the term for a group of notes that are very close to one another. On the piano, several neighbouring notes are played at the same time.

▶ Audio Track **12** | Rhythm Check **5** | Workout **6/7** | Sight Reading **8**

23

UNIT 4: The Magic Note Line

Reading music made easy

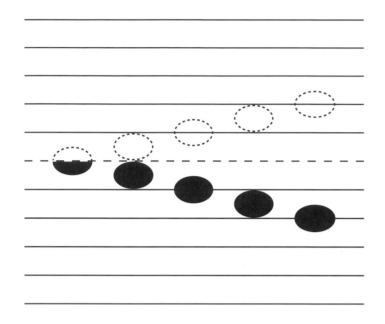

ACTION CORNER

As well as the 5 stave lines for each hand, you will see an extra dotted leger line here between the two music staves. This is called Middle C.

Experiment

Hold a mirror on the dotted line. What do you see? Yes! You see a reflection of notes for the right hand in the mirror.

Middle C 5-Finger Position

T2 page 16

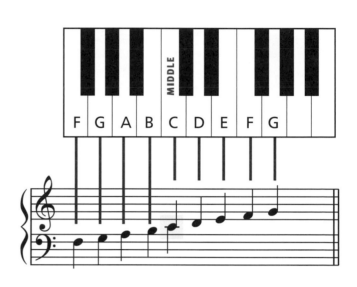

PLAYING
CORNER

Put both thumbs on middle C and the other fingers on the neighbouring white keys. With middle C as a starting point in both hands you can now read the notes quite easily.

For the RH
going upwards
on the white keys

Middle C is a line note, it lies on the line.
The next note up, D, is a space note and lies between two lines.
E is another line note, F is a space note and the note G, a line note.

For the LH
going downwards
on white keys

Middle C is a line note, as in the RH.
The next note down, B, is a space note.
A is another line note, G is a space note, and the note F, a line note.

Remember

From one white key to the next, upwards or downwards, there is always a change from a line note to a space note or space to line.

Rain, Rain, Go Away

English Nursery Rhyme
Arr.: HGH

Moderato   Name notes

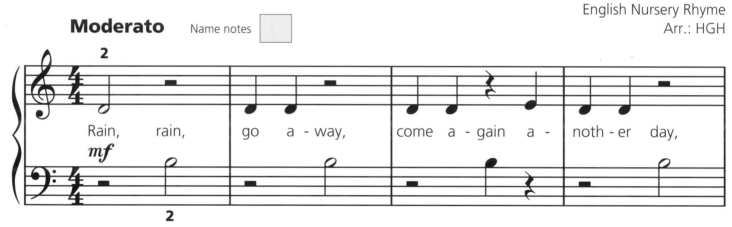

Rain,   rain,   go a - way,   come a - gain a - noth - er   day,

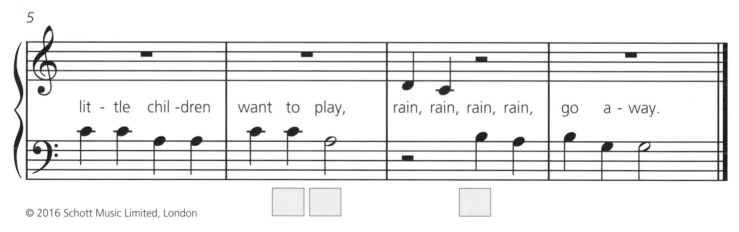

lit - tle chil -dren   want to play,   rain, rain, rain, rain,   go   a - way.

Accompaniment   With Accompaniment, student plays one octave higher than written.

= 160

Hurihuri

This is a traditional Maori song performed by children.

from New Zealand
Arr.: HGH

Allegro

Hu - ri - hu - ri,   hu - ri - hu - ri
Ko - re   ra - wa,   ko - re   ra - wa,

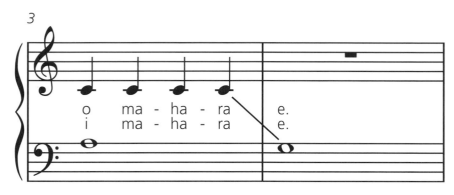

o   ma - ha - ra   e.
i   ma - ha - ra   e.

1.

Ki - te ta - u,   ki - te ta - u,   ki - te ta - u   e.

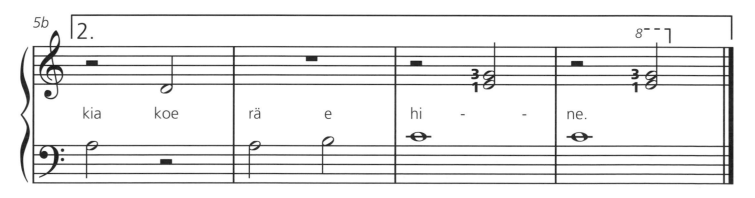

2.

kia   koe   rä   e   hi - - - ne.

     *) Originally, this song would have been sung whilst playing a traditional Maori stick game.

▶ Audio Track **15**

Oragna Fiagata Fa*

Wolfgang Amadeus Mozart (1756-1791)
Arr.: HGH

Moderato

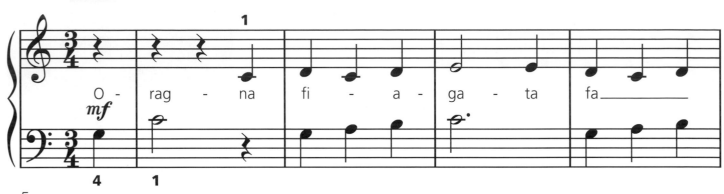

*) Mozart was three years old when he wrote this song. Every evening, before going to bed, he jumped onto his father's lap and pulled his ears until he began to hum the second part to this melody. The title doesn't make sense, as little Wolfgang made up the language himself. In any case it sounds amusing and a little Italian.

Wolfgang Amadeus Mozart was an Austrian composer and one of the great musical geniuses of all time. His father *Leopold* travelled with him and his sister *Nannerl* across Europe and introduced them as brilliant young musicians.

UNIT 5: Quaver/Eighth Note

stem → ♪ ← flag
← filled-in note head

T2
page 19

Two quavers/eighth notes
equal the value of a crotchet.

♩ 1 beat   ♪♪ 1 beat

Several quavers are usually connected with a beam rather than
each one having a flag. Quavers are played twice as fast as
crotchets. The second quaver is counted with the syllable 'and'.

beam

♪ ♪ = ♫   ♪ ♪ = ♫

count: 1 and   1   and

Minuet

P2
page 13

Jean-Philippe Rameau (1683–1764)
Arr.: HGH

Moderato

count: 1 and 2 and 3 and

5

Jean-Philippe Rameau was a French composer. He composed many different types of pieces, including
operas and keyboard works. The **minuet** is a graceful dance in 3/4 time for two people.

30

▶ Audio Track **17** | Rhythm Check **8** | Sight Reading **10**

What is the title of this piece?

World-Famous Melody

Traditional Song from the USA
Arr.: HGH

Allegretto

© 2016 Schott Music Limited, London

allegretto = moderately fast

Pause / Fermata
Hold the note on a little longer than written.

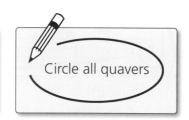
Circle all quavers

The Railway

T2
page 20–23

Allegro

Georges Frank Humbert (1892–1958)

poco a poco cresc. al Fine

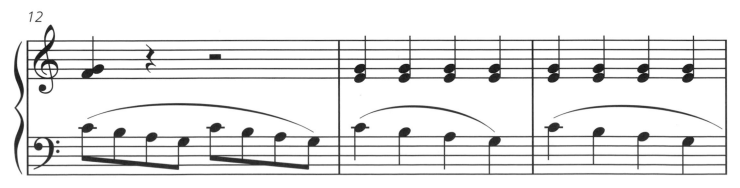

▶ Audio Track **19** | Rhythm Check **10** | Workout **9**

poco a poco = gradually, little by little

COMPOSING CORNER

Compose the missing bars of HURRY UP! It is quite easy, and fun. Then write your name above the piece – Congratulations!

Hurry up!

Composer: ....

Longing Waltz

Allegretto

HGH

marcato

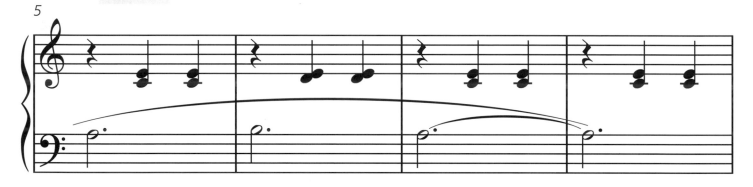

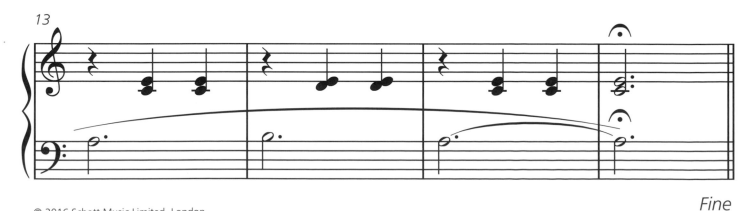

Fine

▶ Audio Track **20** | Rhythm Check **11** | Sight Reading **11**

marcato = marked, emphasized

D. C. al Fine

Melody

from *L'ABC du Piano*

Theme

T2 page 26/27   D2 page 12/13

Félix Le Couppey (1811–1887)

Moderato

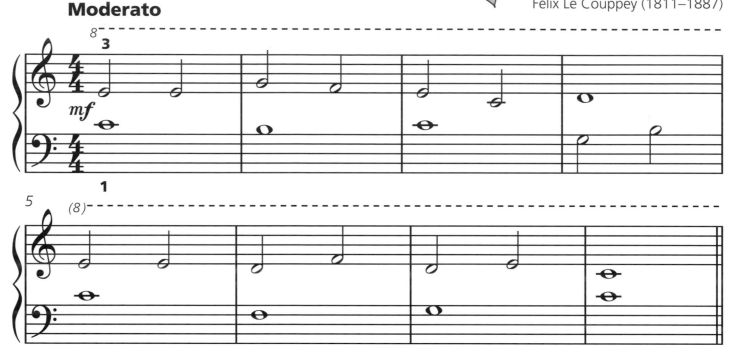

Variation

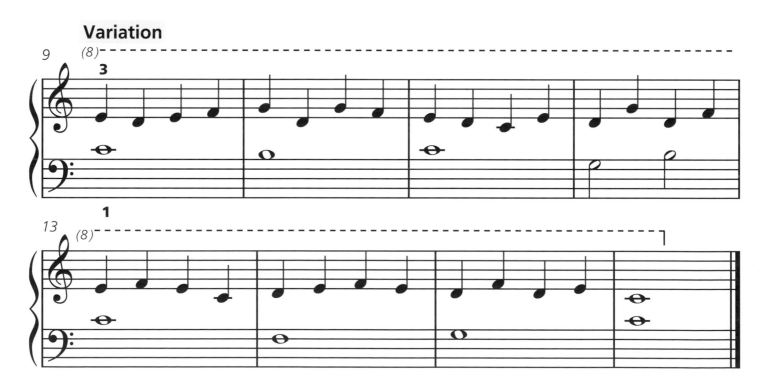

Félix Le Couppey was a French pianist and composer.
He wrote many educational works for piano.

▶ Audio Track **21** | Workout **10**

Variation

A musical **variation** is the changing or ornamenting of a musical theme, for example, by altering the melody, the rhythm or the harmony. Pieces composed in this way are often called Variations.

UNIT 6:
G 5-Finger Position

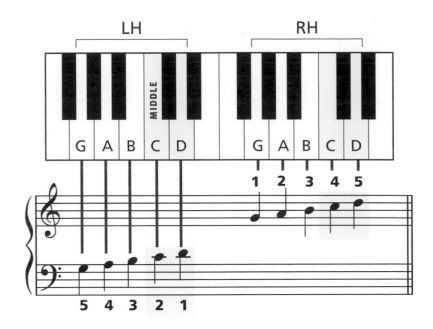

G Position Exercise

 page 75, No. 10

HGH

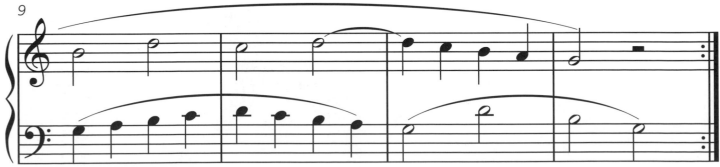

mf

▶ Audio Track **22**

Presto

Daniel Gottlob Türk (1750–1813)

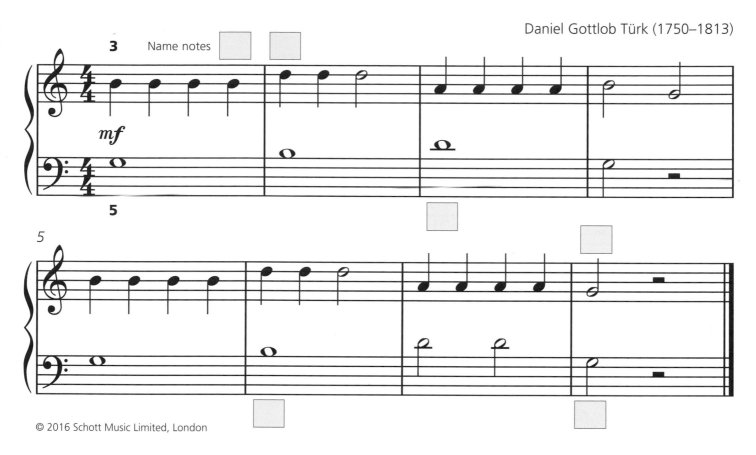

Name notes

Daniel Gottlob Türk was a German piano teacher and composer. His most popular works include a piano method and a large number of pieces for piano students.

presto = very fast

▶ Audio Track **23**

Banks of the Ohio

Allegretto

American Folk Song
Arr.: HGH

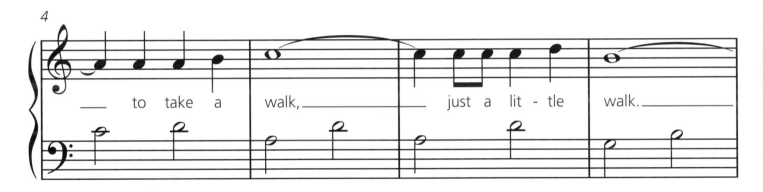

▶ Audio Track **24** | Rhythm Check **12**

Flash Cards 2: Notes

The *Flash Cards* can be used to provide further practice in note reading, with musical symbols/terms and rhythm patterns. You can collect the cards from each book.

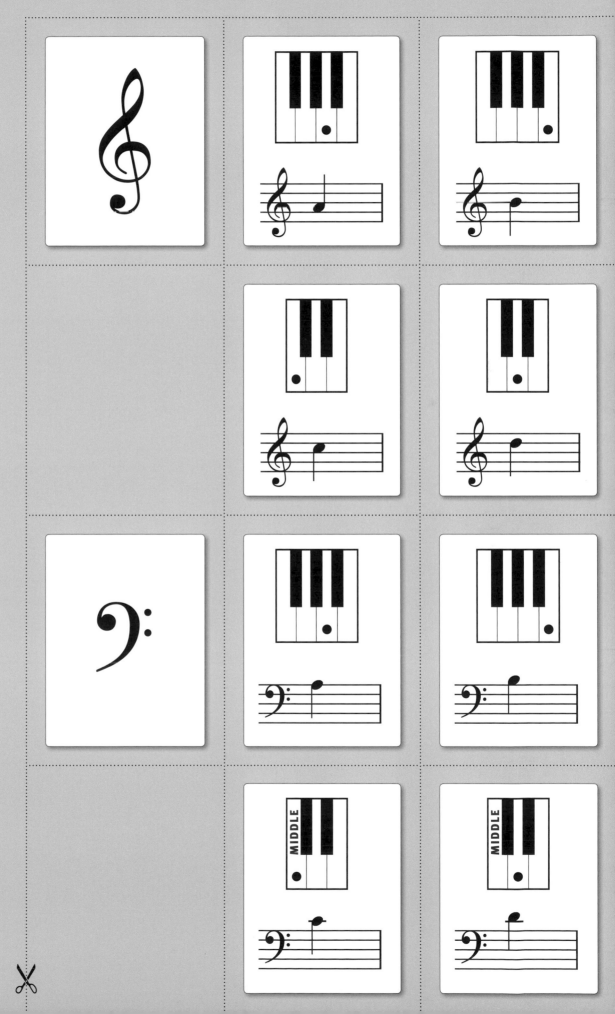

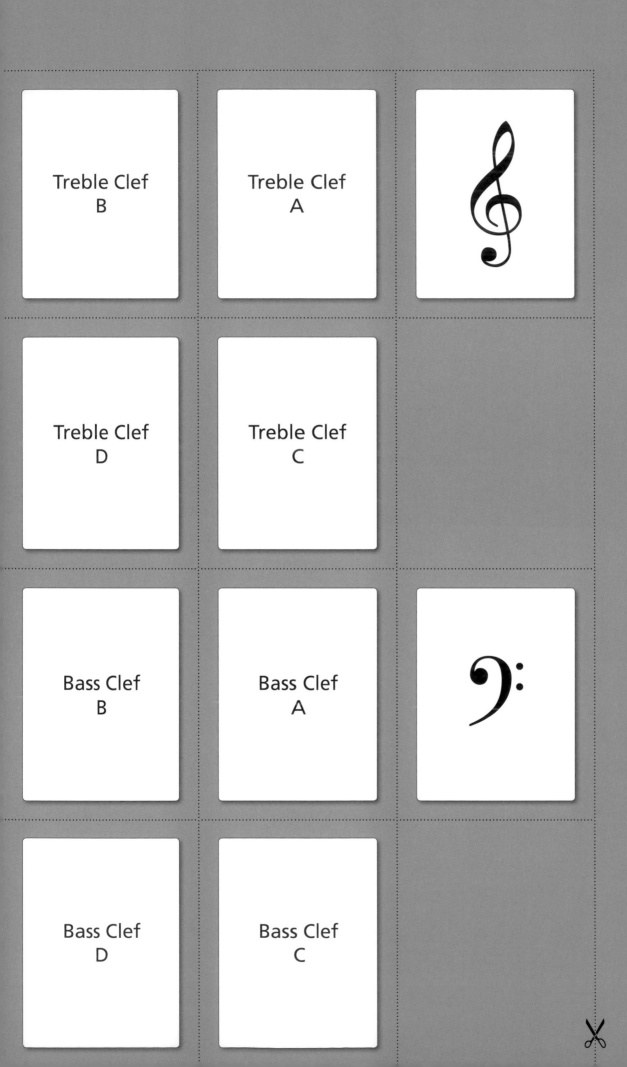

Flash Cards 2: Musical Symbols/Terms (1)

The *Flash Cards* can be used to provide further practice in note reading, with musical symbols/terms and rhythm patterns. You can collect the cards from each book.

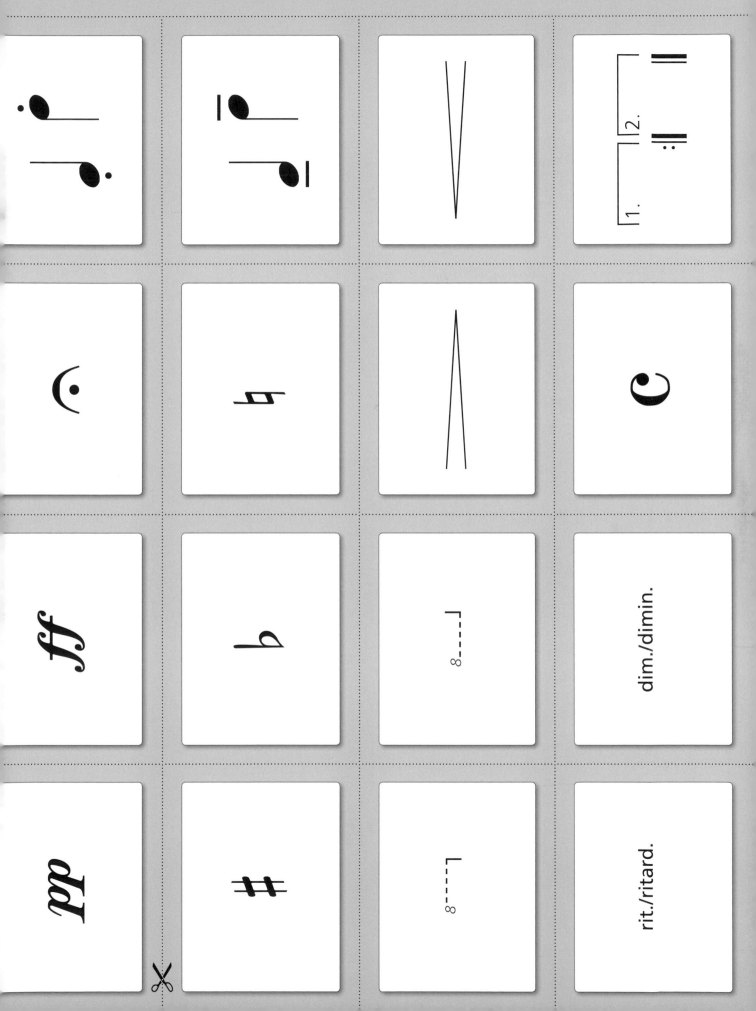

staccato
= short, detached

Fermata/Pause
= Hold the note on
a little longer.

tenuto
= An instruction indicating
that the note should be held
for its full value.

Natural sign
= A natural sign cancels a flat
or a sharp from a preceding
note. Play the original white
key again.

crescendo
= increasing in volume,
getting louder

decrescendo
= decreasing in volume,
becoming softer

If the end of a repeated section
is different to the first time,
numbered brackets can be
added. The first time you play
the part beneath bracket 1,
the next time you miss out
bracket 1 and immediately go
on to bracket 2.

$$\frac{4}{4}$$
alternative means of
indicating 4/4 time

**Octave
Transposition sign**
= Play the note or notes
that appear above this sign
an octave (= 8 notes) lower
than written.

Flat sign
= A flat sign preceding
a note lowers it
by a half step/semitone.

fortissimo
= very loud

diminuendo
= same meaning as
decrescendo

**Octave
Transposition sign**
= Play the note or notes that
appear below this sign
an octave (= 8 notes) higher
than written.

Sharp sign
= A sharp sign preceding
a note raises it
by a half step/semitone.

pianissimo
= very quiet

ritardando
= gradually getting slower

Flash Cards 2: Musical Symbols/Terms (2)

The *Flash Cards* can be used to provide further practice in note reading, with musical symbols/terms and rhythm patterns. You can collect the cards from each book.

maestoso	Interval of a Second	Interval	A–B–A
dolce	Presto	Interval of a Fifth	Variation
poco a poco	Allegretto	Interval of a Fourth	Upbeat/ Anacruisis
marcato	Adagio	Interval of a Third	Articulation

majestically, dignified

tenderly, sweetly

gradually, little by little

marked, emphasized

Distance of two notes

very fast

moderately fast,
a little bit faster
than moderato

slowly, unhurried

Distance between two notes

Distance of five notes

Distance of four notes

Distance of three notes

Ternary form
= This is an A-B-A-form, that is, theme A is introduced, followed by a contrasting B theme, returning finally to the A theme again.

A variation is the changing and ornamentation of a musical theme, for example by altering the melody, the rhythm or the harmony.

An upbeat or anacrusis is an incomplete bar at the beginning of a piece of music. Together with the final bar of the piece, it usually makes up a complete bar.

The joining and separation of notes

Flash Cards 2: Rhythm

The *Flash Cards* can be used to provide further practice in note reading, with musical symbols/
terms and rhythm patterns. You can collect the cards from each book.

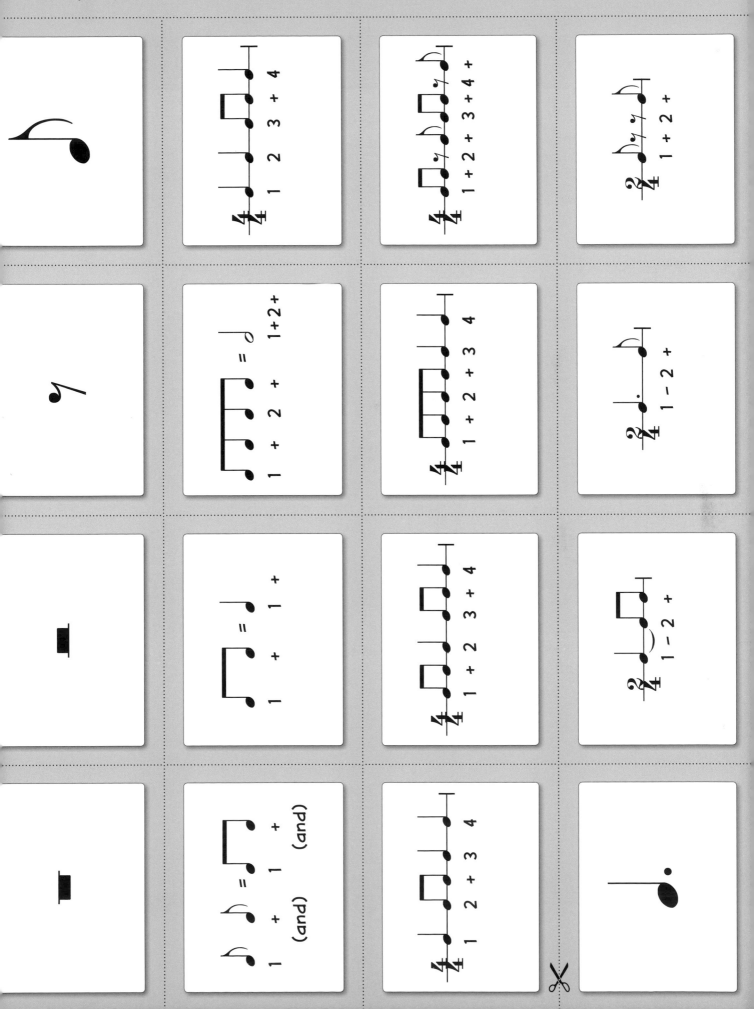

Quaver/Eighth note
= lasts for half a beat

Clap the rhythm
and count out loud

Clap the rhythm
and count out loud

Clap the rhythm
and count out loud

Clap the rhythm
and count out loud

Quaver/Eighth rest
= lasts for half a beat

Clap the rhythm
and count out loud

Clap the rhythm
and count out loud

Clap the rhythm
and count out loud

Clap the rhythm
and count out loud

Minim/Half rest
= lasts for two beats

Clap the rhythm
and count out loud

Clap the rhythm
and count out loud

Clap the rhythm
and count out loud

Clap the rhythm
and count out loud

Semibreve/
Whole rest
= A semibreve/whole rest
always corresponds to the
duration of a complete bar.

Clap the rhythm
and count out loud

Clap the rhythm
and count out loud

Clap the rhythm
and count out loud

Dotted crotchet/
quarter note
= Lasts for one
and a half beats

With Lots of Emotion

D2 page 14–17   **P2** page 15

Dolce

HGH

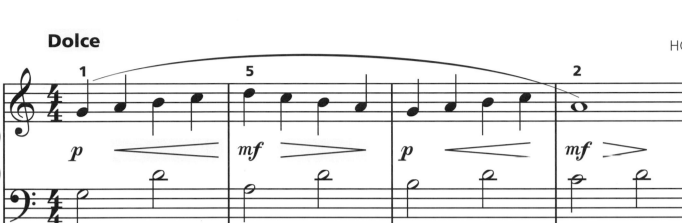

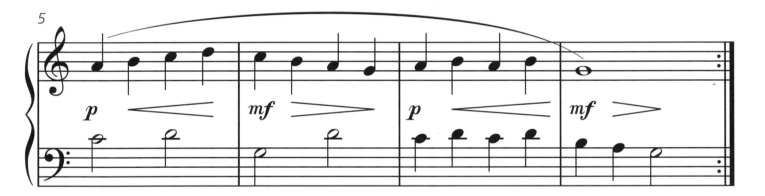

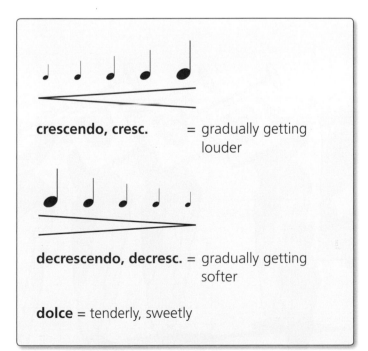

crescendo, cresc. = gradually getting louder

decrescendo, decresc. = gradually getting softer

dolce = tenderly, sweetly

March of a Prince

HGH

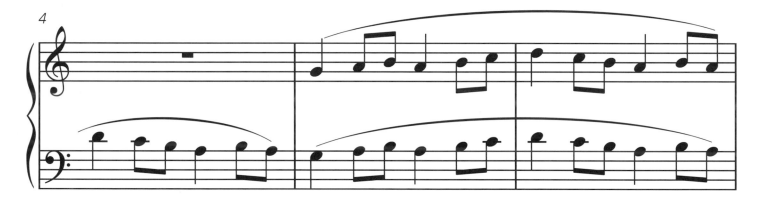

maestoso = majestically, dignified

42

▶ Audio Track **26** | Rhythm Check **13**

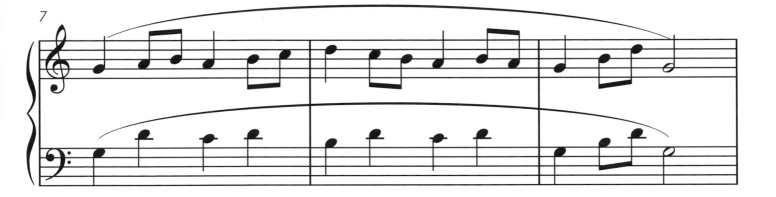

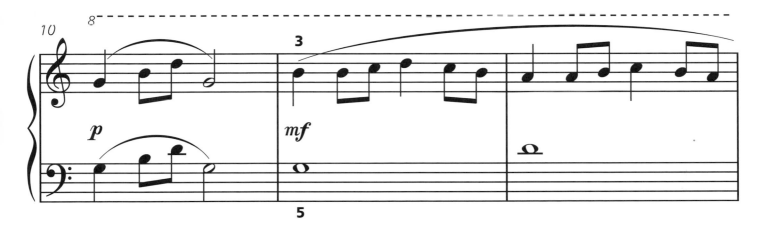

Cheerleaders' Parade

HGH

Allegro

Fine

D. C. Fine

▶ Audio Track **27** | Rhythm Check **14**

Quaver/Eighth Note Rest

Cheerleaders' Parade

COMPOSING CORNER

Transpose CHEERLEADERS' PARADE into the C position. The distance between the notes, the direction of the notes and the fingering stay the same. Try playing the piece from memory.

Allegro

etc.

UNIT 7:
Independence of the Hands

Independence Exercise

HGH

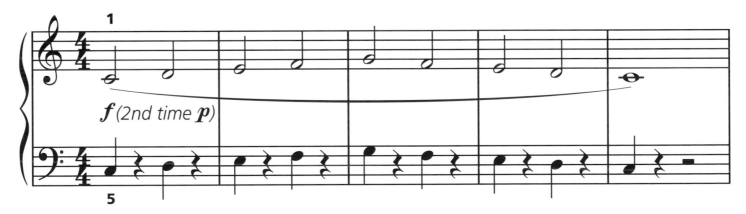

f (2nd time p)

© 2016 Schott Music Limited, London

▶ Audio Track **28** | Rhythm Check **15**

Articulation

Articulation is the joining together, and separating of notes. The two most important kinds of articulation are legato and staccato.

staccato is indicated by a dot above or below the note. It means that the notes should be short and detached.

TECHNIQUE CORNER

When playing staccato, the key is released quickly. The wrist makes a small, quick upwards movement. The finger then returns naturally to the key and rests there.

Articulation Exercise

P2 page 18

HGH

Up Hill and Down Dale

Allegretto

HGH

48

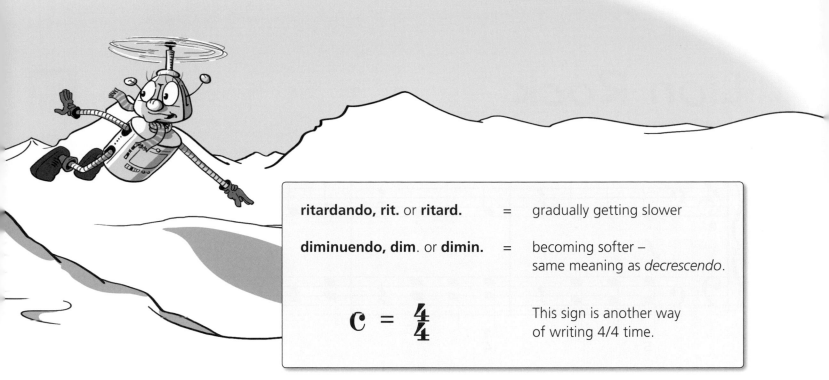

ritardando, rit. or **ritard.**	=	gradually getting slower
diminuendo, dim. or **dimin.**	=	becoming softer – same meaning as *decrescendo*.
¢ = $\frac{4}{4}$		This sign is another way of writing 4/4 time.

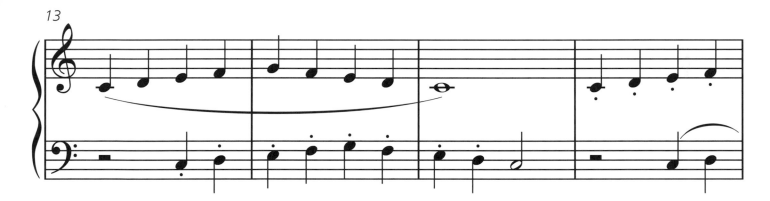

Lion Rock

P2 page 20/21

Allegretto

HGH

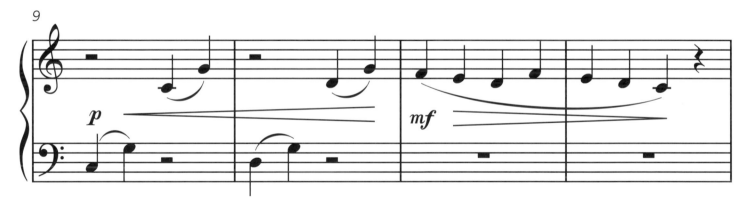

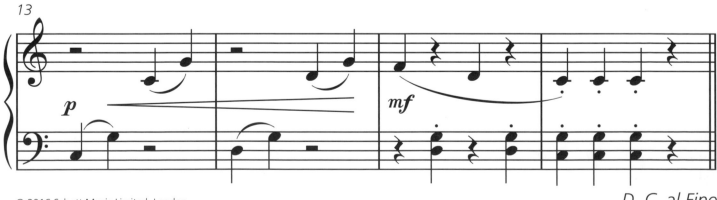

D. C. al Fine

▶ Audio Track **31** | Rhythm Check **16**

Canario

Joachim van den Hove (ca. 1570–1620)
Arr.: HGH

Andante

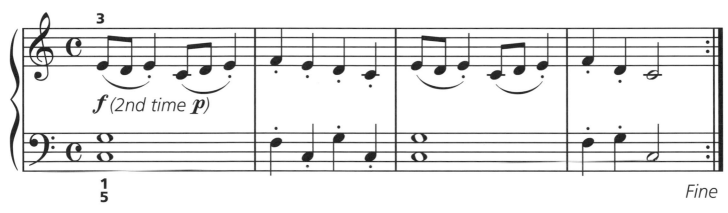

f (2nd time p)

Fine

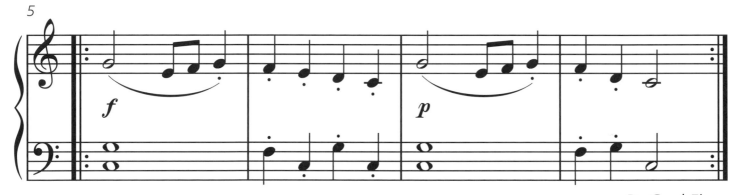

*D. C. al Fine
without repetition*

Joachim van den Hove
was a Dutch composer and lute player.

UNIT 8: Sharp Sign ♯

A **sharp sign** before a note raises it by a semitone/half step.
Play the note immediately to the right on the keyboard – either black or white.
The sharp sign applies throughout the bar in which it appears unless it is cancelled by a natural sign.

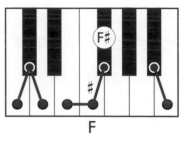

F

●—● = semitone step/
halftone or half step

Little Turtle Walk

D2
page 20/21

HGH

Adagio

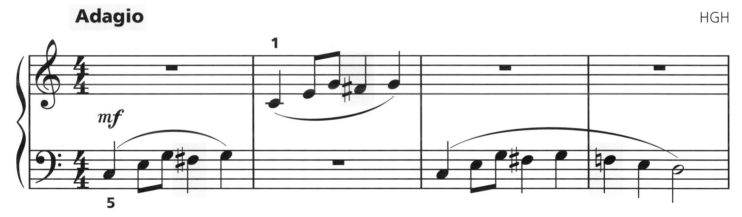

mf

rit.

© 2016 Schott Music Limited, London

adagio = slowly, unhurried

Natural sign ♮

A **natural sign** cancels both sharp and flat signs. This means that you should return to playing the original white key.

▶ Audio Track **33** | Rhythm Check **18**

Circle all sharp signs

A Marching Band is Coming

T2 page 32–35

Moderato

HGH

▶ Audio Track **34** | Rhythm Check **19** | Workout **13** | Sight-Reading **14**

Goodbye Winter

German Folk Song
Arr.: HGH

Allegretto

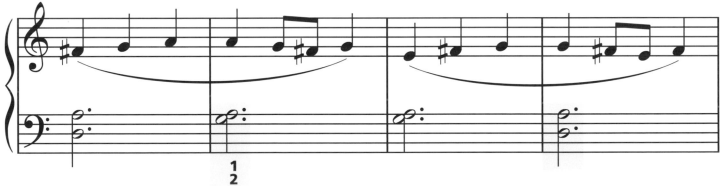

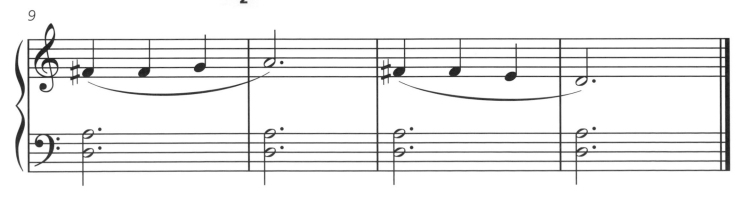

▶ Audio Track **35**

COMPOSING CORNER

Play the piece GOODBYE WINTER also using these four accompaniment patterns. Make sure that you change the interval at the places highlighted in colour. Experiment with other possible combinations or invent new ones.

Surprise Symphony

Theme from the 2nd movement of Symphony No. 94

Joseph Haydn (1732–1809)
Arr.: HGH

Andante

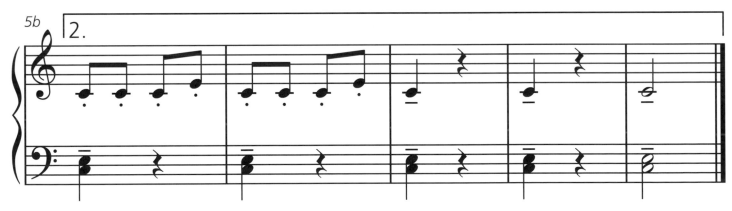

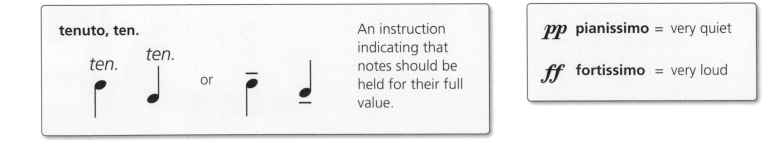

| **tenuto, ten.** | | An instruction indicating that notes should be held for their full value. |

pp **pianissimo** = very quiet

ff **fortissimo** = very loud

▶ Audio Track **36**

Joseph Haydn was a famous Austrian composer and a friend of Mozart. The *Surprise Symphony* is so called due to the sudden loud strike of the kettle drum at the end of a quiet section. Haydn was a humorous man, and thought of this joke to keep the audience on its toes!

William Tell

Circle **pp** and **ff**

Gioachino Rossini (1792-1868)
Arr.: HGH

Allegro

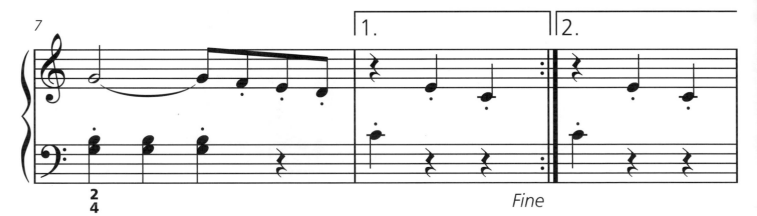

Fine

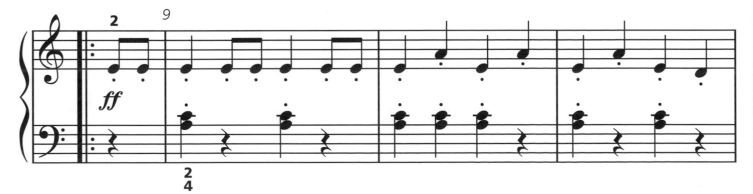

▶ Audio Track **37** | Rhythm Check **20**

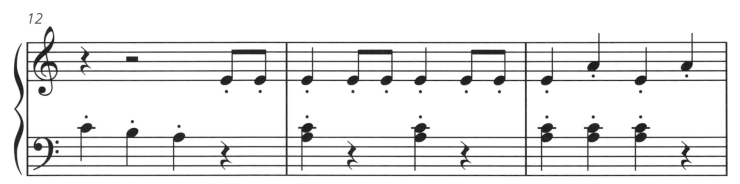

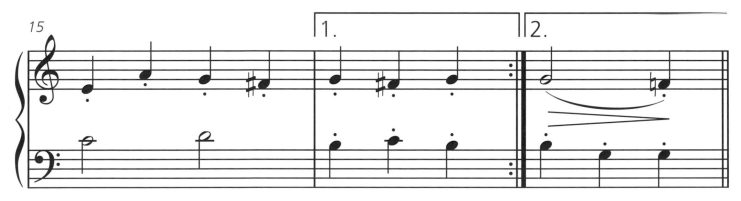

D. C. al Fine

Gioachino Rossini was an Italian opera composer. His most famous operas are *The Barber of Seville* and *William Tell*.

UNIT 9: Flat Sign ♭

A **flat sign** before a note lowers it by a semitone/half step.
Play the note immediately to the left on the keyboard – either black or white.
The flat sign applies throughout the bar in which it appears *unless* it is cancelled by a natural sign.

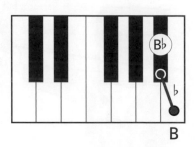

Rock around the Piano

T2 page 36/37 | P2 page 22–25

HGH

© 2016 Schott Music Limited, London

▶ Audio Track **38** | Rhythm Check **21** | Workout **14** | Sight Reading **15**

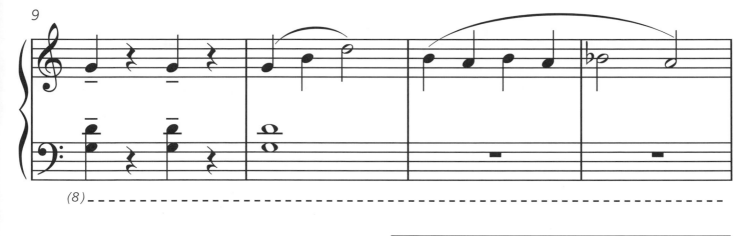

61

Inspector Key

Mysterious

HGH

*) When the sign *15 _ _ _* (Ital. quindicesima) appears under a note or group of notes, play the notes two octaves lower than written.

▶ Audio Track **39**

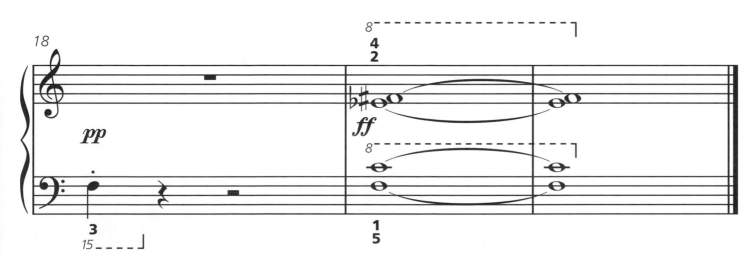

UNIT 10: Dotted Crotchet/ Quarter Note

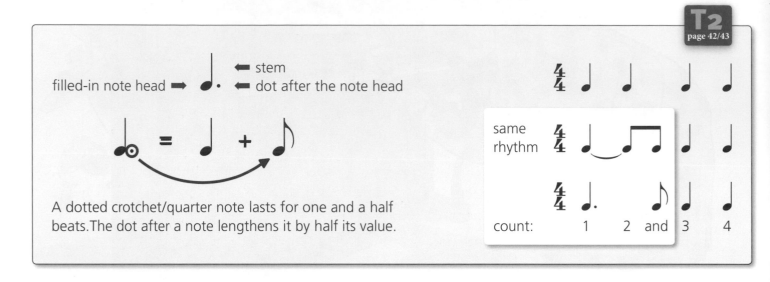

T2
page 42/43

filled-in note head ➡ ← stem
← dot after the note head

A dotted crotchet/quarter note lasts for one and a half beats. The dot after a note lengthens it by half its value.

same rhythm

count: 1   2   and   3   4

Air

Circle all flat signs

Theme from *Water Music*

George Frideric Handel (1685–1759)
Arr.: HGH

© 2016 Schott Music Limited, London

*) **Air** is the French term for melody.

George Frideric Handel was a German composer who travelled widely throughout Europe. He lived in England for almost 50 years writing operas, oratorios and instrumental pieces.

Andante grazioso

T2 page 44/45 **D2** page 26/27 **P2** page 29

Wolfgang Amadeus Mozart (1756–1791)
Arr.: HGH

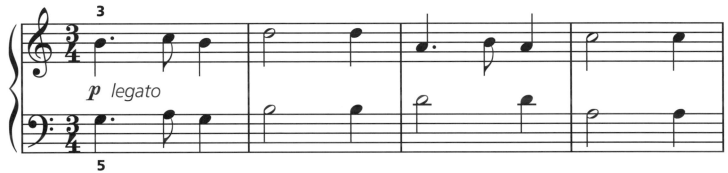

p legato

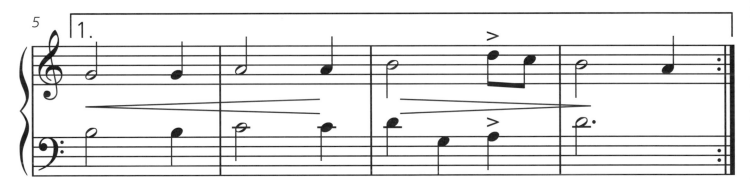

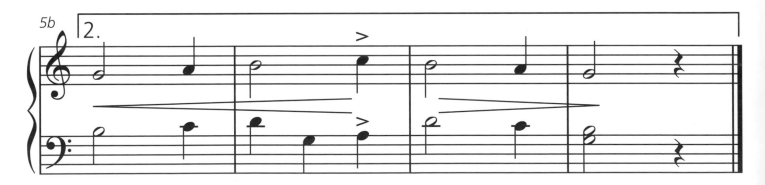

grazioso = graceful, charming

▶ Audio Track **41** | Rhythm Check **23**

Scherzo

from *Melodic Exercises* Op. 149, No. 6

Anton Diabelli (1781–1858)
Arr.: HGH

Allegro

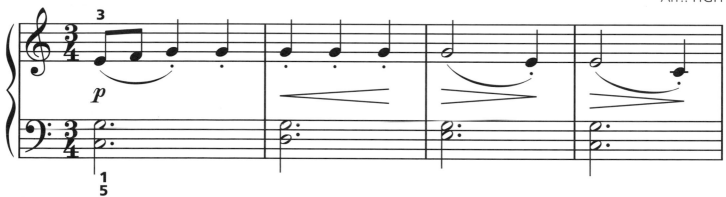

Anton Diabelli was an Austrian music publisher, music teacher and composer. His *Melodic Exercises* Op. 149 are still popular in piano lessons.

▶ Audio Track **42** | Rhythm Check **24** | Workout **16**

Trumpet Tune

page 77, No. 15–18

Maestoso

Jeremiah Clarke (ca. 1674–1707)
Arr.: HGH

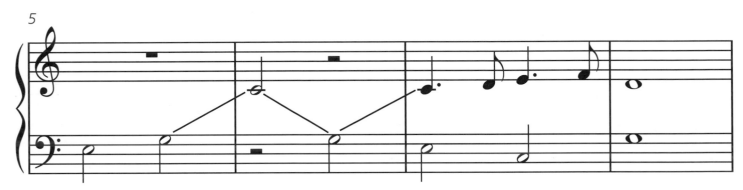

(2nd time rit.)

Jeremiah Clarke was an English composer and organist at St. Paul's Cathedral and the Chapel Royal in London. He also wrote music for the theatre such as this *Trumpet Tune*.

▶ Audio Track **43** | Rhythm Check **25**

Trumpet Tune

COMPOSING CORNER

Transpose TRUMPET TUNE into the D and F positions.
Only the first four bars are notated here.
You have to take care of the rest. Have fun!

D 5-Finger Position

Maestoso

etc.

F 5-Finger Position

Maestoso

etc.

69

Daily Finger Fitness 2

These are progressively graded daily finger exercises for developing finger strength and independence, evenness, accuracy and speed of playing, as well as articulation and general musicality.

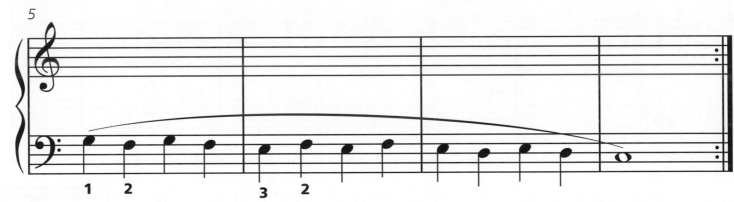

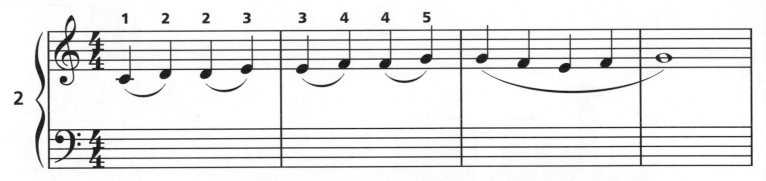

70

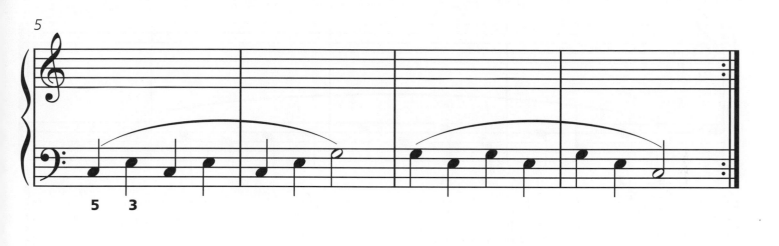

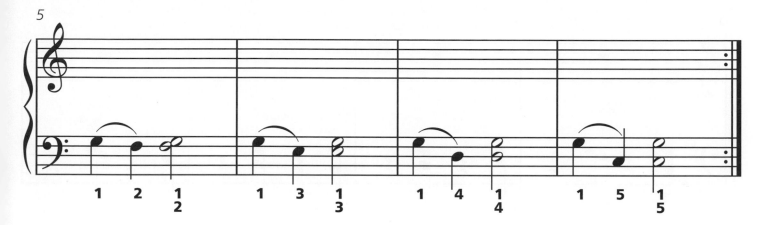

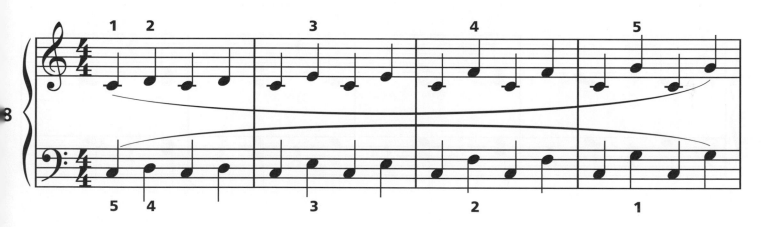

73

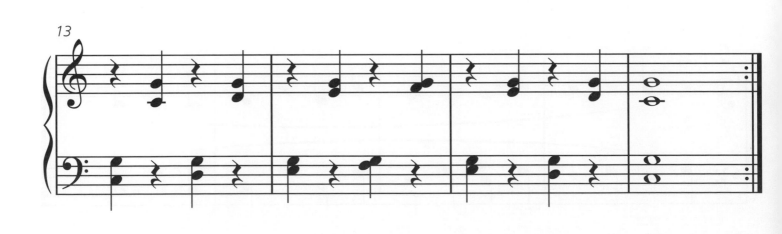

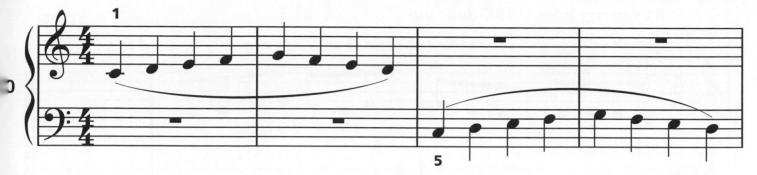

Fine

D. C. al Fine

8 Exercises from *L'ABC du Piano*

Félix Le Couppey (1811–1887)

11

legato

12

13

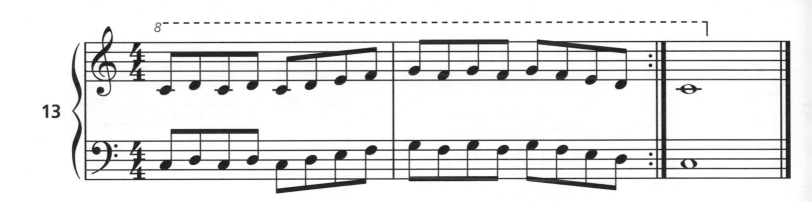

14

Important Words and Signs

	Adagio	Slowly, unhurried
	Allegretto	Moderately fast, a little bit faster than moderato
	Articulation	The joining and separation of notes
 𝄽	Crotchet/Quarter note rest or quarter rest	A crotchet/quarter note rest lasts for one beat
 <	crescendo, cresc.	Increasing in volume, getting louder
 >	decrescendo, decresc.	Decreasing in volume, becoming softer
dim./dimin.	diminuendo	Same meaning as *decrescendo*
	dolce	Tenderly, sweetly
 ♩.	Dotted crotchet/quarter note	A dotted crotchet/quarter note lasts for one and a half beats. The dot after a note lengthens it by half as much again.
	Fifth	Distance of five notes
♭	Flat sign	A flat sign preceding a note lowers it by a semitone/half step
ff	fortissimo	Very loud
C = **4/4**	4/4 time	Another way of indicating 4/4 time
	Fourth	Distance of four notes
	grazioso	Graceful, charming
	Interval	The distance between two notes
	Maestoso	Majestically, dignified
	marcato	Marked, emphasized
 𝄼	Minim/Half note rest or half rest	A minim/half note rest lasts for two beats
♮	Natural sign	A natural sign cancels a flat or a sharp from a preceding note. Play the original white key again.
8----┐	Octave transposition sign	Play the note or notes that appear below this sign an octave (= 8 notes) higher than written

78

8_ _ _ ⌐	Octave transposition sign	Play the note or notes that appear above this sign an octave (= 8 notes) lower than written
𝄐	Pause/Fermata	Hold the note on a little longer
pp	pianissimo	Very quiet
	poco a poco	Gradually, little by little
	Presto	Very fast
♪	Quaver/Eighth note	A quaver/eighth note has a filled-in note head with a stem and a flag. Two quavers equal the value of a crotchet.
♉	Quaver/Eighth rest or eighth rest	A quaver/eighth note rest lasts for half a beat
rit./ritard.	ritardando	Gradually getting slower
	Second	Distance of two notes
▬	Semibreve/Whole note rest or whole rest	A semibreve/whole note rest always means the duration of a complete bar
♯	Sharp sign	A sharp sign preceding a note raises it by a semitone/half step
stacc. ♩	staccato	Short, detached
ten. ♩	tenuto	An instruction meaning that the note should be held for its full value
A-B-A	Ternary form	Ternary form is a type of structure in three parts. It has an A-B-A shape. Theme A is introduced, followed by a contrasting B theme, before returning to the A theme again
	Third	Distance of three notes
	Upbeat/Anacrusis	An upbeat or anacrusis is an incomplete bar at the beginning of a piece of music. Together with the final bar of the piece, it usually makes up a complete bar.
	Variation	A musical variation is the changing or ornamenting of a musical theme, for example by altering the melody, the rhythm or the harmony.

Certificate of Merit

Student _____

has successfully completed

Book 2 of the PIANO JUNIOR method

Teacher _____

Date _____

My favourite piece was _____